presents

CRUMPY

This edition published by Parragon Books Ltd in 2015

Parragon Books Ltd
Chartist House
15–17 Trim Street
Bath BA1 1HA, UK
www.parragon.com

Written and illustrated by Emily Portnoi
Edited by Frances Prior-Reeves

ISBN 978-1-4748-0426-4

Printed in China

Moodles presents

GRUMPY

MOODLE YOUR TROUBLES AWAY

Bath · New York · Cologne · Melbourne · Delhi
Hong Kong · Shenzhen · Singapore · Amsterdam

WELCOME
to your moodle book.

'What is a moodle?' I hear you ask. Well, a moodle is just a doodle with the power to change your mood. Be it grumpy to glad, happy to sad or glad back to mad. Cheaper than therapy, quicker than chanting chakras, tastier than a cabbage leaf and sandpaper detox, and less fattening than chocolate cake!

The moodle: a simple thing that can really turn your day around.

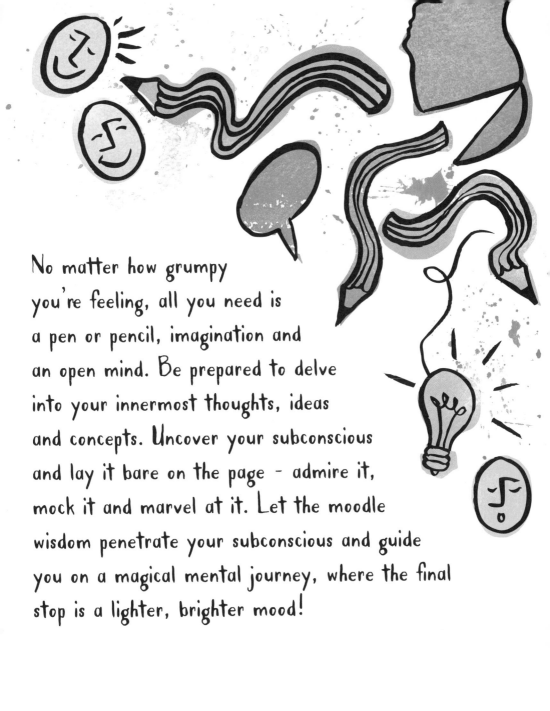

No matter how grumpy
you're feeling, all you need is
a pen or pencil, imagination and
an open mind. Be prepared to delve
into your innermost thoughts, ideas
and concepts. Uncover your subconscious
and lay it bare on the page – admire it,
mock it and marvel at it. Let the moodle
wisdom penetrate your subconscious and guide
you on a magical mental journey, where the final
stop is a lighter, brighter mood!

Moodle your GRUMPIEST frown in the middle of the page. Then turn the book upside down.

Now draw in the rest of your face. VOILÀ!

Draw one thing that has really brought you down today. Then tear out this page, screw it into a tight ball and throw it into the bin - did you get it in first time?

For a more challenging and cathartic version of this moodle, place the bin on a high shelf or use a very small bin.

Don't be UNDER the weather.

Moodle yourself above the clouds.

1. Get a pencil.
2. Scribble all your frustration onto this page.
3. Rub it out.
4. Repeat until all anger is erased.

Colour **ALL** the grass green.

This page has given you lemons.

So why not make
lemonade?

CREATE A MONSTER
THAT IS THE EMBODIMENT
OF YOUR MOOD!

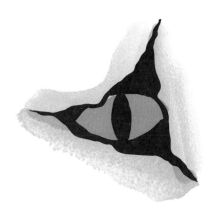

This ice lolly is about to have a meltdown.

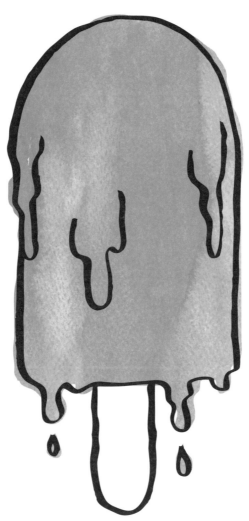

What can you moodle to save it?

Design your own fortune teller.
Make every fortune fortunate!

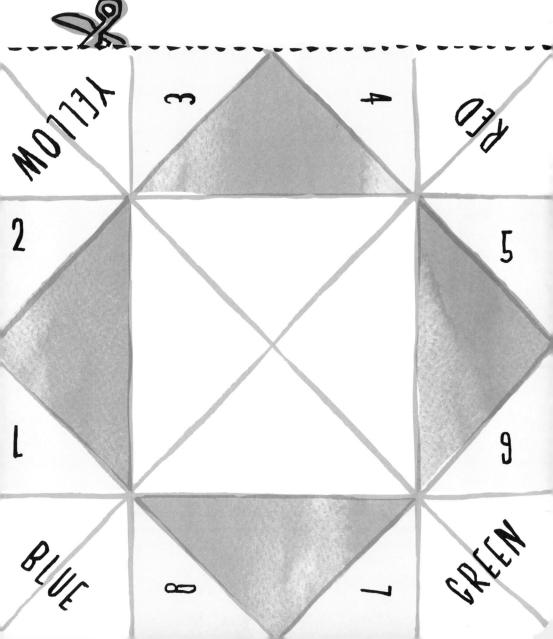

HOW TO MAKE YOUR FORTUNE TELLER

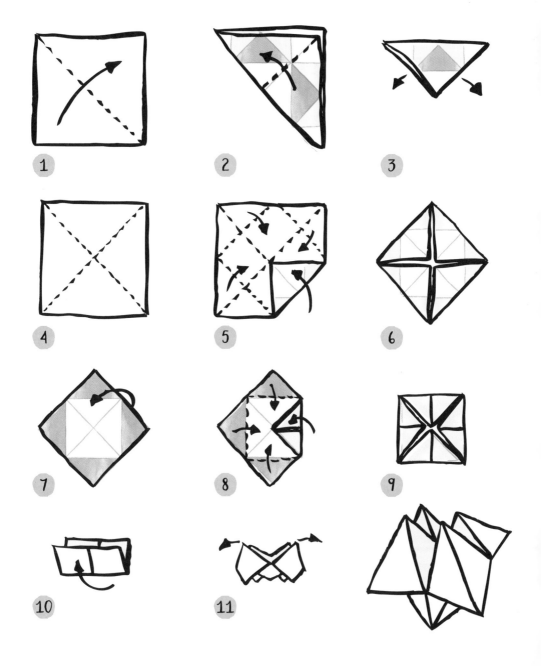

Moodle yourself as a flower –
looking pretty and smelling great is bound to perk you up.

ACKNOWLEDGE YOUR MOODS
and they will pass quicker.
Moodle an emotion a day.

Counting to ten is a great way to calm yourself down, BUT moodling to ten is even better.

YOUR PENCIL IS POSSESSED BY
THE **BAD-MOODLE** DEMON,
LET HIM TAKE OVER.

Fill this page with an explanation of why you're in a bad mood; then SCRIBBLE out every other word and read it back.

Draw a **GINORMOUS** grin on this face.

Cut along the dotted lines and wear as a mask!

DRAW THE WORD **GRUMPY** IN THE
HAPPIEST STYLE YOU CAN MUSTER.

Try again.

DRAW **THREE THINGS** THAT YOU ARE GRATEFUL FOR TODAY.

LOST

MY GOOD MOOD

Description:

Last seen:

If you had an **AWESOME SIDEKICK** you'd feel **TRULY SUPER.**

Create your ideal sidekick here.

DUMP YOUR EMOTIONAL BAGGAGE.

Moodle all your negative emotions onto these bags.
Tear out this page, take it on holiday and leave it behind.

Sketch the faces these **moody eyes** belong to
— see if you can cheer them up a bit.

Look on the bright side
— draw with neon pens.

YOU'RE TOP OF THE TRUMPS.

AWESOMENESS: %

SECRET SKILL:

BEST FEATURE:

Moodle your own stats card.

Here's your FANTASY CALENDAR; fill it in with your ideal life.

Be more creative! Nobody's marking this stuff.

This tomato is having a BAD DAY.
Draw it a tomato friend to cheer it up.

KNOW SOMEONE WHO COULD REALLY DO WITH THEIR FACE REARRANGING?

Well, sketch them here; then cut along the dotted lines and reconstruct into an abstract arrangement.

Exercise can really LIFT YOUR SPIRITS.

Lift this book above your head five times.
Well done! Now put your name on this medal.

Need to find your HAPPY PLACE?

Sketch it here; then you'll always be able to find it.

BECOME THE SUPERHERO
OF YOUR OWN COMIC.

WHAT WOULD YOUR
SUPERPOWER BE?

DRAW AS IF YOU WERE
FOUR-AND-THREE-QUARTER-YEARS OLD.

Misery loves company.
Find a friend and moodle together.

challenge your own identity.

Moodle 6 possible new signatures for yourself.
1 must contain a cat. 2 must contain hieroglyphs.
1 must be a smiley face. 1 must be in orange.

EMBRACE the NEGATIVE!
Only draw the shapes in-between objects.

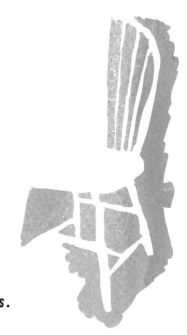

BAD HAIR DAY?

Give each of these heads a different style.

FILL UP THIS BISCUIT BARREL.

Then dip your hand in whenever you need a little sweet comfort.

Try seeing things from a **different** point of view. Put your head between your legs and draw what you see — careful you don't get too dizzy.

Moodle your ultimate everyday hero here,

using your favourite body parts and characteristics from people you know.

Make this **SPIKY** cactus the flowering variety.

CHEER UP **Mr Grumpy Gills** BY MOODLING HIM SOME FISHY FRIENDS.

Take leave of your senses.
Moodle with your eyes closed.

Moodle **five wishes** for your future onto these crystals. Cut them out and hold them tight for ten minutes a day.

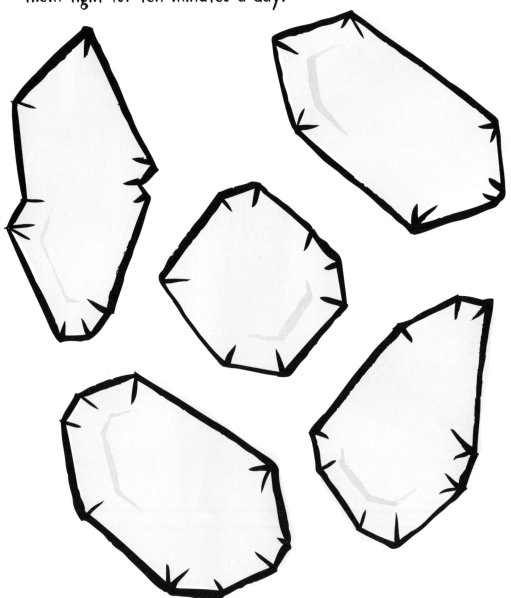

Fill your head ENTIRELY with happy thoughts and moodles.

Make sure there's no room at all for negative thoughts to creep in.

Focus on the **IMPORTANT** details.

MOODLE YOUR FAVOURITE COMPLIMENT.
Then tear this page out and
stick it on your mirror.

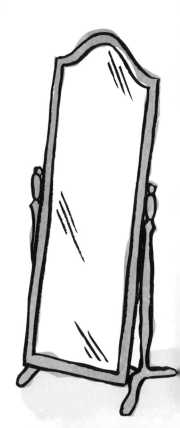

Smile — it may never happen!
Moodle your smile here.

A QUICK TRICK TO BANISH THE BLUES:

draw around your toes and then moodle them into a family of foxes.

TIDY HOME, TIDY MIND!

Moodle all of your mess
neatly onto these shelves.

MOODLE YOUR GUARDIAN ANGEL.

Here's a COSMIC BLACK HOLE.

Moodle what you would throw in.

Repeatedly write the line
'My anger WILL disappear,'
over and over on this page,
until it is no longer legible.

Draw a picture entirely in shades of
AGGRESSIVE RED.

Time to DECLUTTER!

Draw the same moodle six times, using one less line each time.

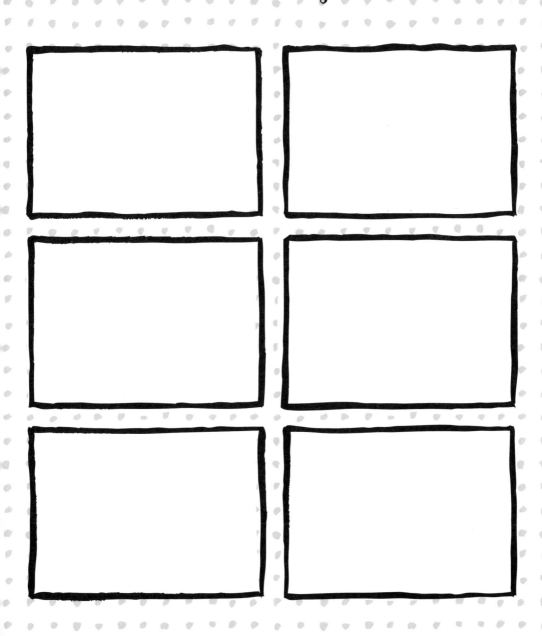

MOODLE THE SUN COMING OUT.

MOODLE A RAINBOW.

MOODLE A
POT OF GOLD.

GET SOME PERSPECTIVE.

Turn these moodles into 3D objects.

Try out all the PENS and PENCILS you own on this page.

Pick your favourite.

Write a letter of forgiveness to yourself.

Moodle yourself a **VERY** long fuse.

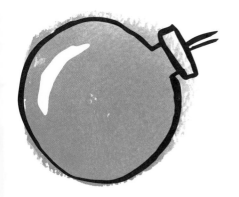

There's nothing like your favourite TV show to cheer you up.
Sketch your **favourite** TV and movie scenes.

Challenge your bad mood to a duel.

Moodle your own rescue from the ISLE OF GLUM.

Count your blessings here.

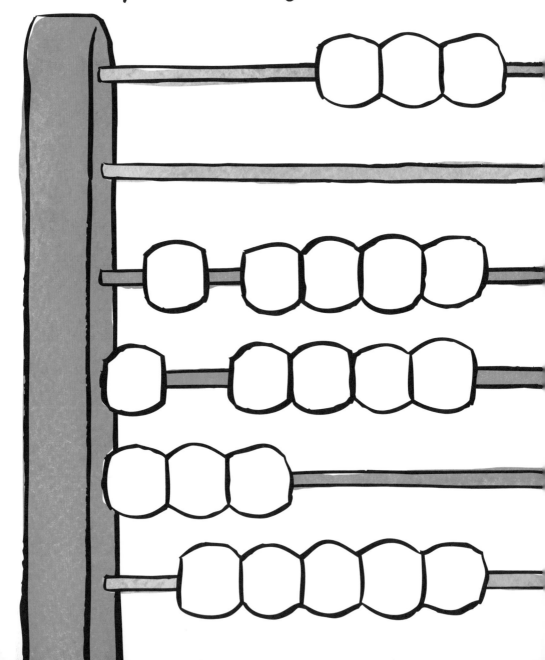

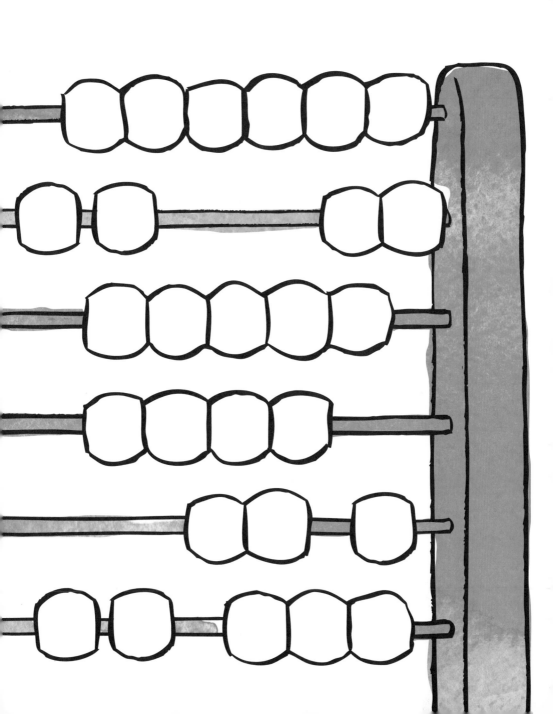

WINNING IS A STATE OF MIND.

Sketch yourself in the number 1 spot on the podium.

GRUMPILY draw a self-portrait; then draw a **GRUMPY** self-portrait.

Which do you prefer?

Shift your focus.

Draw something you can
see far in the distance.

MOODLE YOUR PET PEEVE; then cut out,

pin up and take aim.

DANCE IS THE PERFECT WAY TO LET GO.
Turn the music up and moodle your best dance moves.

Will the sun come out tomorrow?

Draw your week's forecast and try to be optimistic.

MONDAY

TUESDAY

WEDNESDAY

THURSDAY

FRIDAY

SATURDAY

SUNDAY

According to Mark Twain,
the best way to cheer yourself up
is to CHEER SOMEBODY ELSE UP!

Draw a funny moodle and show it to as many
people as possible — one person is bound to laugh.

Picture yourself on this raft,
floating slowly downstream.

Draw your PERSONALITY.

HELP THESE BIRDS BUILD THEIR NEST.

1. Tear out this page.
2. Scrunch it into a tiny ball.
3. Unfold.
4. Draw along the crease lines.
5. Find the beauty in the imperfect.

Moodle your **ULTIMATE** ice-cream sundae.

Draw someone you think
could do with a good

SLAP

Then slap the page.

OK, so you're **stuck in a bit of a hole**...
moodle yourself a ladder to climb out.

Are you getting enough sleep?

Moodle as many sheep as you can before you doze off.

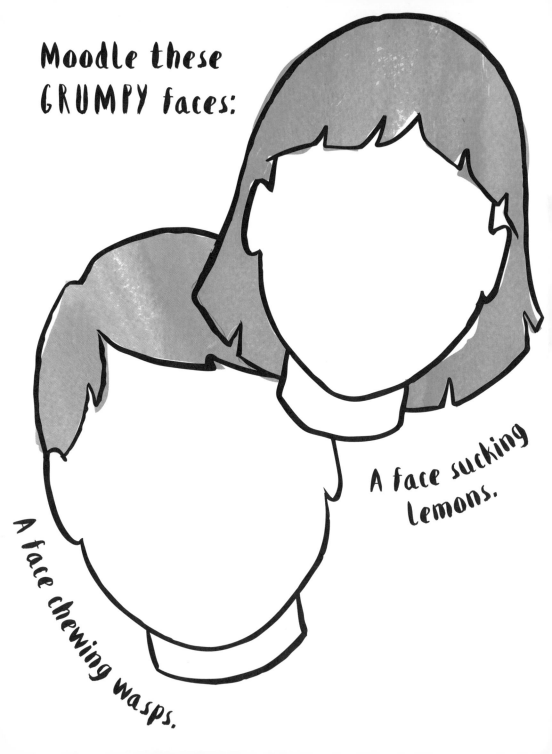

Moodle these GRUMPY faces:

A face sucking lemons.

A face chewing wasps.

A face that could curdle milk.

A face eating sour grapes.

MOODLE YOUR FAVOURITE SONG.

Make these **BLOBS** your new creature friends.

Enjoy the **little things.**

Draw five things smaller than your thumbnail.

Moodle yourself a BRAND-NEW SPECIES of animal; make it the CUTEST, FLUFFIEST and SMILIEST animal possible.

Name it and make notes of its characteristics.

QUICK DRAW.

Draw the first thing you think
of when you read these words:

GLOOM

PUDDLE

HOLLOW

All moodles complete and wisdom absorbed,
you will by now have reached a state of complete
un-grumpiness. Perhaps you are floating on a higher
mental plane, unable to even recall what
had annoyed you in the first place.

To complete the ultimate moodle and karmic
U-turn, find someone who looks a bit grumpy
and tell them how awesome they are.